Diagnostic Reading Analysis
Reading Booklet

Diagnostic Reading Analysis
Reading Booklet
(Forms A & B)

Mary Crumpler & Colin McCarty

HODDER
EDUCATION
AN HACHETTE UK COMPANY

Acknowledgements

Original reading passages written by Mary Crumpler, Marie Lalloway, Mike de la Mare and Jenny Vaughan.

Illustrations by Paul Archer.

Photos by Corbis (page 34: © Bettmann - CORBIS; page 83: © Patrick Ward – CORBIS); Action Plus sports images (page 41); EMPICS – SportsChrome (page 82); and NASA (page 88).

Orders please contact Bookpoint Ltd, 130 Milton Park, Abingdon, Oxon OX14 4SB. Telephone: (44) 01235 827720. Fax: (44) 01235 400454. Lines are open from 9.00 to 5.00, Monday to Saturday, with a 24-hour message answering service. You can also order through our website www.hoddereducation.co.uk

British Library Cataloguing in Publication Data

A catalogue record for this title is available from the British Library

ISBN 9780340882573
Impression number   14
Year   2014

Printed in Spain for Hodder Education an Hachette UK company, 338 Euston Road, London NW1 3BH.

LISTENING COMPREHENSION

I made a cake for my sister. She was six.

The cake was good.

She showed it to my brother.

He took half of it!

We were having a great day. We were told to keep together, but Ali ran ahead.

Suddenly he stopped, his mouth wide open.

Just in front of him was a cow with huge horns.

He stayed near us after that!

Listening comprehension C

Last night, a magical balloon carried me to a beautiful garden, in another world. I heard birds singing, and saw fishes swimming in a clear pool. I felt such happiness!

Suddenly, I awoke – in my own bed.

But I wasn't disappointed. I had remembered something important.

It was my birthday!

When I was young and nosey, I explored Mum's cupboard. I discovered a box containing an old plate. I dropped it and it shattered. I replaced it with one from the kitchen.

Yesterday was my birthday. Mum presented me with the box, carefully wrapped. "Great-grandfather wanted you to have this when you were thirteen. Be careful – it's extremely valuable."

Shirt ironed, hair combed and skin scrubbed, I approached very nervously. I hesitated. I raised my hand without actually trembling – I wasn't that anxious! But I did require one hand to steady the other as I pressed the doorbell.

Music throbbed, and I heard occasional screeches of female laughter. Male voices shouted anecdotes followed by cheers or contradictions – "Yeah, bet you did!"

The door opened. A vision stood before me. Well, I knew who it was really, but she looked especially beautiful tonight. Then her face smirked with amusement.

I knew I shouldn't have let my sister choose my clothes.

Diagnostic
Reading Analysis

READING: FORM A

On Sunday, I went to play football.

My big brother was in goal.

I tried to kick the ball hard.

I fell over in the mud.

Bats sleep all day in trees or old barns.

When it is getting dark, they go out.

They fly about looking for food to eat.

Anna drew a map. She put it into a bottle.

She threw it into the river near her house.

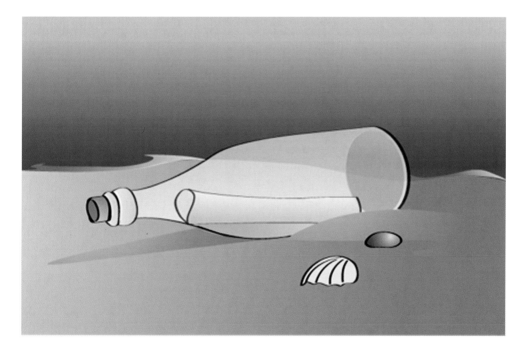

Harjit found the bottle on the beach.

He looked at the map and tried to follow it.
Where would it take him?

How to make a cup of tea

- Boil some water.

- Place a tea bag in a cup.

- Pour on the water. Be careful!

- Take out the bag.

- Add milk and sugar if you like.

- Drink it hot and enjoy it!

We made a big mistake.

We went for a walk on the beach. It became very stormy.

The waves were too high and came up over our knees. I was scared.

We had to climb over the rocks to escape.

For achieving

THIRD PLACE

in schools' art competition

Well done!

Lydia Potts

Third Place
ART
competition

Well done!

Last term, Purple Class drew and painted birds for a competition at the art gallery.

This week, they were invited to see all the pictures and find out if they had won any prizes.

Donna's drawing came third.

When I was young, my grandfather bought a carpet.

"It's magic," he said. "Sit on it, and wish for anything you like – happiness, friendship, riches. Choose whatever you want."

I thought for a long time. Then I jumped onto the carpet and made my wish.

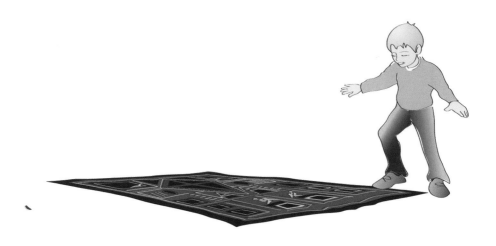

Guess what happened the next day!

The potter is making a bowl. She uses soft clay and kneads it until there are no air bubbles left in it.

When her bowl is just right, she fires it in a hot oven.

After that, the clay becomes very hard, so it is impossible to change its shape.

It was early morning. The travellers looked across the desert. There was sand, as far as the eye could see.

Then, unexpectedly, they heard distant voices. They had company! Should they be suspicious?

A group of camels was coming towards them, the riders dressed in white. Were these people friends?

Imagine a world without telephones. It seems impossible –
but that was how things were until 1876.

That was the year a Scotsman called Alexander Bell made
an important discovery. He found out how to transmit
sounds along a wire, using an electric current.

This remarkable invention changed the world for ever.

Carla's cat was perched nervously on the end of a branch, too terrified to descend. A rescue was attempted – a rope was used to pull the branch lower.

Unexpectedly, the rope broke. The cat disappeared into the distance.

Several gardens away, Lance was complaining angrily he hadn't received a cat for his birthday. At that moment, his present arrived.

Two thousand years ago, a volcano erupted in Italy. Most of the inhabitants of nearby towns escaped, but some, including gladiators in chains, could not. They breathed in hot and poisonous gases. Wet ashes covered their dead bodies.

The ashes set to stone. The bodies crumbled away. The spaces that remained show exactly how the people lay when they collapsed.

During the Second World War posters were everywhere: "Careless talk costs lives." People thought anyone who behaved strangely was transmitting information to the enemy.

Thomas had seen Mrs Mayer in her kitchen, muttering into a suitcase. This convinced him she must be a spy.

Eventually, Thomas discovered his neighbour was reading old love letters from her husband fighting in Europe.

Science on the move

These are some of the scientific principles involved in riding a bicycle.

The helmet shape reduces the effect of air resistance.

Chemical energy from food provides the driving force.

Brakes create friction to slow the wheels down.

Air pressure in the tyres acts as a shock absorber.

Forces operate the brakes through the action of levers.

Systematically extracting his favourite pen from an inside jacket pocket, and relocating the spectacles from the top of his head to the bridge of his nose, Inspector Hansom surveyed the scene.

Upturned furniture, ransacked drawers and absent electrical items all suggested burglary.

He methodically trawled the room from left to right, front to back, scratching rapid, almost unreadable notes. Something was wrong. He knew it instinctively. It was all too perfect, like a scene from a poor quality television drama.

Amita skips training and jumps to victory

Triple jump superstar Amita Patel leapt to gold for her country yesterday, despite last weekend's injury scare.

The athlete was in despair when serious fitness doubts threatened her prospects of even participating in the finals. She abandoned her usual gruelling training schedule to avoid worsening the calf problem. The gamble paid off. Enforced rest, together with gritty determination and four painkilling injections, prepared Amita for a magnificent performance to carry off top prize.

A wall of water triumphed above me, pausing to glory in its immense destructive power, before descending upon my home, my transport – my boat. The deck split and splintered. The raging waters swallowed me, then spat me contemptuously to the surface.

The storm subsided. I drifted in and out of consciousness, buffeted by gentler waves. My face was crisped with salt and roasted in the sun. I may have passed hours like this, or even days.

Eventually, the weightlessness of the sea became the soft solidity of sand. The burning sun gave way to shade – or, more precisely, someone's shadow.

In this century, people around the world still go hungry or even starve; not because there is a worldwide shortage of food, but as a consequence of poverty. Our global agricultural production exceeds the food requirements of our whole population. Logically, there should be no starvation.

If we could distribute equally all the food produced in the world, each person would receive at least one and a half times their essential calorie intake every day.

Realistically, this is not a practical solution. But, how can nutritious food, at fair prices, be made available to everyone today and in future generations?

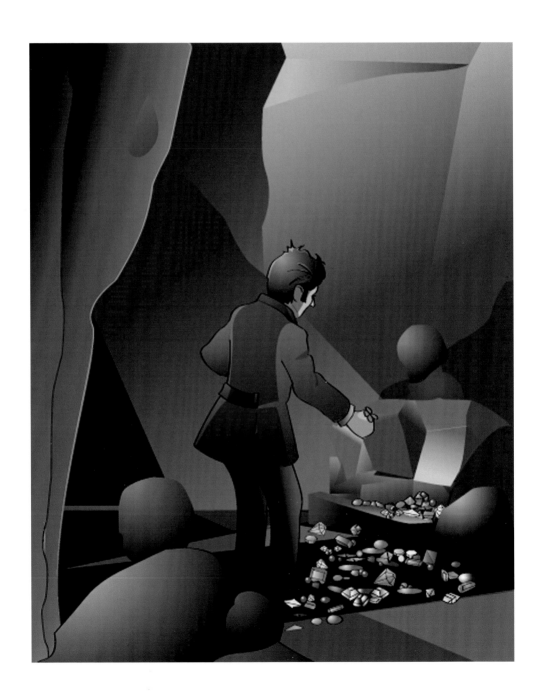

Legend held that the towering black stone guarded a hoard of precious jewels.

At midnight on the longest day, impossible things would occur. The immobile rock would relinquish its bonds, and all living witnesses would turn to stone – except those bearing a four-leafed clover.

Bernard had zealously sought this charm and now clasped the leaf. Awestruck, he marvelled as the rock arose from its pit and lumbered towards the river. The moonlight flickered from emeralds, rubies and diamonds.

Bernard clambered into the cavern. He stood, mesmerised by the riches around him.

The crushing weight of the stone lurched steadily homeward....

Outside, crowds were cheering, but a respectful silence fell over the congregation as Elizabeth entered. Courtiers from every corner of the country had jostled, shoulder to shoulder, to gain positions close to the aisle and so make their presence known to the new queen. As she passed by, they turned, smiling and bowing to show their loyalty.

She was slight, youthful and not a little shy. Had it not been for her unfaltering regal bearing, she might have been overwhelmed by the ornate coronation robes. Yet the determination in her expression signalled that she would impress all on this day.

Diagnostic
Reading Analysis

READING: FORM B

On Saturday, we went to the park.

I flew my kite. It was green.

Poor dad had to go up the tree
to get it.

Rats can make good pets,
but you must look after them.

They need food, and clean water
to drink.

They like playing in their cage.

Tim heard a sound.

He looked around. It was coming from
a litter bin.

Was something trapped in there?

Tim could not see inside. He pushed and
pulled, but the top would not move.

Who could help him open it?

Making a hat

- Cut a strip of card. It must fit round your head.

- Cut out some paper shapes.

- Stick them on to the card with glue.

- Add glitter if you like.

- Join the ends of the card.

- Have fun!

Reading: fiction 4

The boys were waiting under a tree. Rain was beginning to fall.

The bus had not come and they were going to be late for school.

They did not know what to do.

Then, suddenly, Tony had a great idea.

Before half term, we enjoyed Book Week.

On Tuesday morning, Patti Green came into school
and helped the children write stories.

She brought some of her books and read them
in assembly. She signed a different one for every
class.

Last week, my friends found a strange pebble in the playground. It was completely white, and almost round.

We took it into the classroom.

Soon, it began to shake and we heard a very faint tapping sound. It started to crack open.

Everyone watched in amazement.

Guess what came out!

I made a mask.

First I blew up a balloon. I tore some newspaper into little pieces and stuck them carefully over half of it.

I did this several times, then left it all to dry overnight.

Next morning, I burst the balloon.

Now my mask was ready to decorate.

Late in the afternoon, we saw an island.

The pilot brought our plane down successfully on the white sandy beach. The land around was covered with massive trees and a carpet of thick undergrowth. Everything was completely silent.

Suddenly, something stirred among the bushes. We held our breath in suspense.

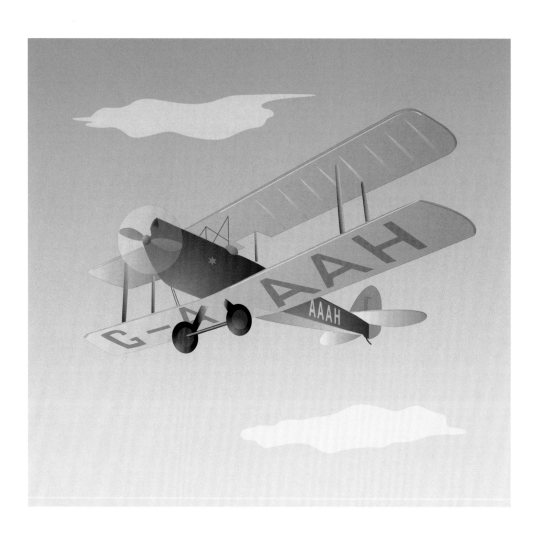

Amy Johnson was the first woman to pilot an aeroplane from England to Australia. This made her famous.

It was a long, dangerous journey to make alone!

On the flight, she had a compass to guide her. She also carried a letter offering ransom money in case she was kidnapped.

My neighbour was extremely pleased with the enormous guard dog he had bought. It barked fiercely and growled at anyone approaching his property.

Unfortunately, when he returned from the football match last Saturday, the dog had disappeared. So had all the furniture in his house.

The person who had sold him the dog was not anywhere to be found, either.

For millions of years, mammoths, giant sloths, beavers the size of bears and other huge mammals roamed America. But, about eleven thousand years ago, they became extinct.

Many scientists believe that this was caused by a change in the climate. Others think differently, however. They say it is not a coincidence that humans first arrived in America at this time.

Two years ago, I overheard Mum ordering expensive boots. My wonderful twin got them for his birthday. All I got was a shirt.

So what? Football is pathetic.

Last year I noticed receipts for computer games. I got trousers.

Who cares? Games are boring.

Today my brother whispered, "She's hiding a dog in the garage!"

He didn't appreciate the socks.

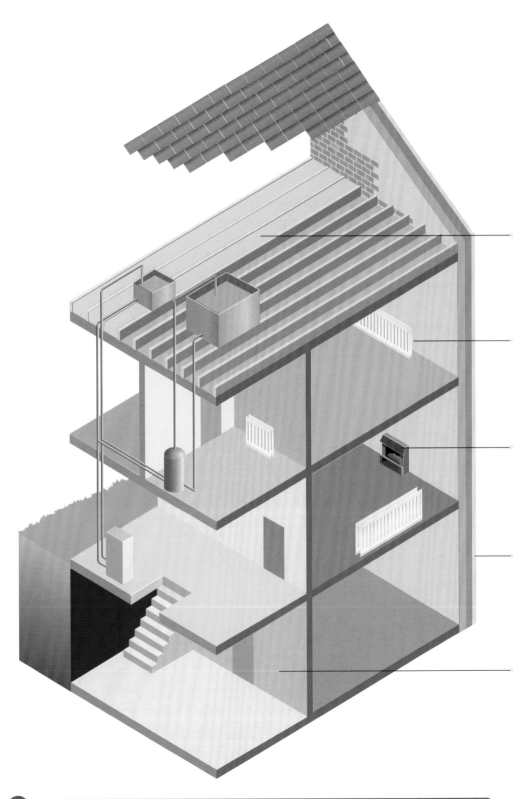

Hot science!

Loft insulation reduces the amount of warmth escaping through the roof.

Radiators work by convection – air is warmed up and then rises. Cool air replaces it, then becomes heated too.

Electric and gas fires give off thermal radiation.

Gaps inside walls help prevent heat being conducted outwards through the bricks.

The temperature is normally lowest in a cellar.

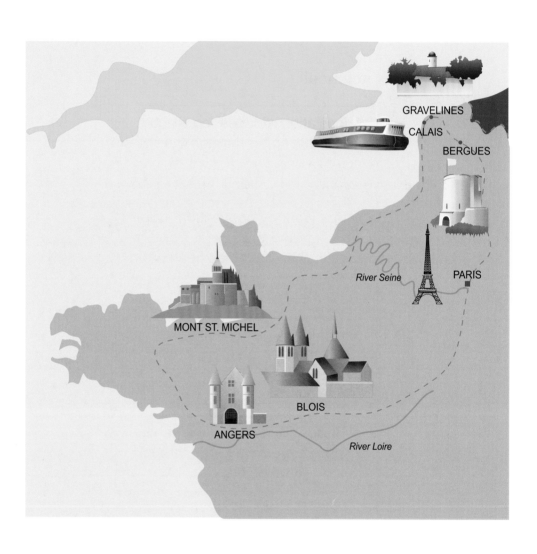

GRAVELINES

CALAIS

BERGUES

River Seine

PARIS

MONT ST. MICHEL

BLOIS

ANGERS

River Loire

After just two days in France, I realised that going on holiday with Sam was a serious mistake. Her insistence that she should always be next to the window of the coach, and her constant whingeing about foreign food, were ruining my holiday and exhausting my patience.

We arrived at an ancient castle, to visit the dungeons. I had not contemplated anything vindictive. But as she trudged along, bombarding me with her complaints, a cunning plan formed in my mind.

A picture of success!

Tennis dynamo Sharon Hing is confident she can make significant progress in the forthcoming French Open – despite being eliminated in the first round for two consecutive years.

Sharon, who is as famous for her emotional outbursts as for her powerful forehand, has been supported by a sports psychologist.

'He has taught me techniques for staying calm and visualising victory,' she enthuses. 'They can try what they like, but nobody's going to rattle my cage this time!'

At first, the changing perspective was absolutely fascinating.

The cathedral spire still dominated the skyline, as if trying to puncture the clouds, but familiar houses and shops had been dwarfed by anonymous office blocks.

Closer by, various scenes unfolded soundlessly below: a couple arguing, storming off, and then reconciling; mischievous children knocking over bins and fleeing; young people in queues shuffling forward, waiting to buy tickets.

However, after an hour, stationary at the top of the big wheel, my interest in humankind was beginning to diminish, replaced by an urgent desire for a portion of chips from the foodstall below.

Around the turn of our century, communication was radically transformed by rapid growth in the use of mobile phones.

But was this technological revolution truly beneficial?

Peer pressure to possess the latest model of phone led to young people pestering their parents with requests to spend exorbitant amounts on these items. Ironically, some newer models quickly became obsolete because they ceased to be fashionable. In extreme cases, thieves resorted to violence in order to acquire the most popular phones.

Teenagers spent hours, and a small fortune, conversing and texting. They seemed to prefer electronic modes of interaction to personal contact!

Few ventured across the moors at night, but Finbar's horse had fallen lame on the journey home.

He knew the desolate wilds were populated by hosts of unnatural creatures who would startle travellers into screaming. Then, entering through the open mouths, the invaders would possess their bodies.

Dusk thickened into impenetrable darkness. Haunting wails echoed from the surrounding rocks, intensifying all the while. Instinctively, Finbar clutched the pendant around his neck – a polished stone – a parting gift from his daughter that morning.

With affection came inspiration. Finbar scrabbled on the ground, seeking round pebbles and cramming them into his mouth.

Millions of people worldwide stared intently at their television screens, acutely aware of how dangerous, and yet how momentous, that first step on the Moon would be.

With apparent confidence, the first astronaut lowered himself from the lunar module to the surface, raising a brief haze of dust. He partly floated, partly walked, with unavoidable slowness, carefully negotiating the unfamiliar terrain in his cumbersome protective suit. A fall that damaged his oxygen supply or immobilised him could prove fatal.

Once safely joined by his partner, the two lunar explorers proudly planted a flag to celebrate the success of their mission.